You Are NOT Your Thoughts

Written by Brian Despard
Designed by Joanne Despard

You Are NOT Your Thoughts

Written by Brian Despard

Designed by Joanne Despard

Photographs by Joanne Despard and C. Przezdziecki

A New Life Design Studio Book, Chicopee, Massachusetts

Website: www.newlifedesignstudio.com ● ISBN: 978-0-615-35934-2 Softcover

This book is dedicated to my family, especially the women in my life who, each in their own way, have made me who I am today. They range in age from 3 years old to 78 years young.

Special thanks to Eva and Erika for always reminding me to "live in the moment."

And also to all the beautiful children who made this picture book possible.

May all of you live in loving-kindness.

Thoughts come and go,

they never last long.

One minute they're here,

the next, they're gone.

When you look up at the clouds in the skies of blue, try to see the whole sky as the clouds pass through.

The clouds are like thoughts.

The sky is like you.

You are
BEAUTIFUL
and
the sky is, too.

However you are feeling,

happy or blue,

we all have many feelings,

it's okay to feel them, too.

Try to feel your body,
from your toes to your head,

when you're

standing up,

sitting down

or lying in

your bed.

Feel it from the inside.
Feel it with your mind.

Always love your body.
Always treat it kind.

When you look at something,

a raisin . . .

. . . or a door,

try to really

see it

as you never have before.

Can you hear the sounds

carried through the air,

and the  silence

in between them?

They are always there.

Can you feel the air all around your skin?

Can you feel the air all around your skin?

Can you feel the air all around your skin?

Can you feel the air all around your skin?

Can you
feel the air
all around
your skin?

Can you feel the air all around your skin?

Can you feel the air all around your skin?

Can you feel the air all around your skin?

Can you feel the air all around your skin?

?
?
?
?

Stop
sometime

and feel it

as you breathe it in.

Everything is changing,

things come and go . . .

. . . just like a river

everything must flow.

This is the moment,

the only one we get,

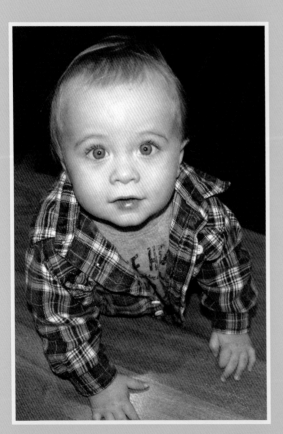

to live, love

and feel, but

the one we

most forget.

Tomorrow isn't here,

yesterday is gone.

Right here, right now

is right where you belong.

It's okay to be still,

to sit and rest awhile.

Breathe in and breathe out,

close your eyes and smile.

Everything's easier

if you practice every day.

Breathe in and breathe out,

and love yourself today!

There's
nowhere
to go.

There's nothing to do.

Breathe in
and smile.

Breathe out
and be you!

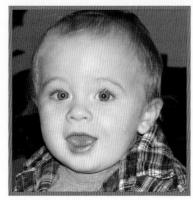

Namasté

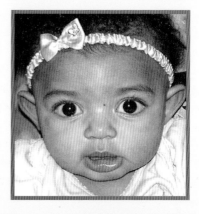

REFLECTIONS

"I love the book; it's beautiful! I can actually see the clouds as thoughts moving in the blue skies of my mind. This book is for children of all ages, and for all the children within us! As we are awakening, learning to breathe and live mindfully, this book brings a loving reminder and smile to the beauty and wonder of each present moment."

In loving gratitude,
Tiana Mirapae
M.Ed., LCSW -- Montague, MA

"As a person who subscribes to Buddhist philosophy, I find it extremely honest and pure. As an educator, I believe this book would be very useful since it opens the doors for so many lessons and activities. I would especially love to use it at the beginning of the year, when we are establishing a community of love and respect in the classroom. I find it very under-standable and kid-friendly. The pictures are excellent. The brightness and colors are sure to captivate the kids!"

Lori Kyle
first grade teacher -- Springfield, MA

"What a wonderful book! It is something really delightful and accessible for little ones. I like the combination of words and pictures."

Ruth Folchman
psychologist and professor -- Northampton, MA